THE MANIFESTATION JOURNAL

KELSEY LAYNE

RADAR

First published in Great Britain in 2023
by Radar, an imprint of
Octopus Publishing Group Ltd
Carmelite House
50 Victoria Embankment
London EC4Y 0DZ
www.octopusbooks.co.uk

An Hachette UK Company
www.hachette.co.uk

Published in the United States
by TarcherPerigee, an imprint of
Penguin Random House LLC,
1745 Broadway, New York, NY 10019, USA

ISBN 978 1 80419 163 7 (Hardback)

ISBN 978 1 80419 164 4 (Trade Paperback)

A CIP catalogue record for this book is available from the British Library.

Printed and bound in the UK

1 3 5 7 9 10 8 6 4 2

This FSC® label means that materials used for
the product have been responsibly sourced.

I could not wait to share this journal with you, as it contains all of the practices I use daily that allow me to manifest my dreams. I really hope that these techniques will help you to turn your dreams into reality too.

Kelsey x

RAISE YOUR VIBRATION

I like to think of the widely used phrase "raise your vibration" as meaning "create a positive energy flow." When you do this, you can vibrate at what is known as a high frequency. Vibrating at a high frequency is an integral part of the manifestation process, as this state of being can help you to be more receptive to going with the flow of your own magical energy, and therefore be at one with your inner being.

To raise your vibration, simply make sure to carve out time for the activities that make you feel alive, excited, and joyful, no matter how big or small.

ENERGY FLOW

Honor the flow of your energy. Some days you may feel upbeat and ready to go, and other days you may feel like resting or moving slowly through your day. Both states are completely natural, and both states are your body's magical way of creating balance. Although slowing down when you desire to manifest something can feel counterintuitive, pushing against the current of your energy can leave you feeling burned out, confused, or even lost.

PRACTICE ALIGNMENT AND GROUNDING ACTIVITIES

Act only when in alignment, because when in this state you are following the path that makes you feel good and is therefore the path of least resistance. This will naturally make the journey of manifestation feel as though you are effortlessly gliding your way to your ultimate destination.

If, however, you find yourself out of alignment and taking directions that do not intuitively sit well, fear not, as this is easily fixed and is just your magical inner compass signaling to you that you need to take some time to ground yourself. There are many activities that can help you to do this, such as spending time in nature, free-flow journaling, and more. Once grounded, you will feel confident in the steps that you are taking to turn your dreams into reality.

PRACTICE DAILY GRATITUDE

Gratitude can allow you to see how far you have already come, and to notice the abundance that you already have.

YOUR
KEYS
TO
MANIFESTATION

* SACRED SPACE *

Use this space to set intentions as your journey begins or free-flow journal.

WEEK BEGINNING ______________________

TO BE IN ALIGNMENT AND GROUNDED, THIS WEEK I WILL:

- ◯ GO OUT IN NATURE
- ◯ MEDITATE
- ◯ ______________________
- ◯ ______________________

I WILL RAISE MY VIBRATION WITH THE FOLLOWING ENERGIZING ACTIVITIES:

I AM GRATEFUL FOR:

____

I WOULD LIKE TO MANIFEST:

THE STEPS I CAN TAKE TO ACHIEVE THIS ARE:

- ◯ ____
- ◯ ____
- ◯ ____

IS ANYTHING MENTALLY HOLDING ME BACK?
DID ANY LIMITING BELIEFS COME UP LAST WEEK?

WHY DO I THINK THIS IS?

WHAT EMPOWERING AFFIRMATION WILL HELP ME TO MOVE FORWARD OR REFRAME THIS LIMITING BELIEF?

FREE FLOW

✳ SACRED SPACE ✳

Record achievements no matter how big or small, reflect, or free-flow journal.

THE POWER IS WITHIN ME

WEEK BEGINNING ____________________

TO BE IN ALIGNMENT AND GROUNDED, THIS WEEK I WILL:

- ○ GO OUT IN NATURE
- ○ MEDITATE
- ○ ____________________
- ○ ____________________

I WILL RAISE MY VIBRATION WITH THE FOLLOWING ENERGIZING ACTIVITIES:

I AM GRATEFUL FOR:

____

I WOULD LIKE TO MANIFEST:

THE STEPS I CAN TAKE TO ACHIEVE THIS ARE:

- ○ ____________________
- ○ ____________________
- ○ ____________________

IS ANYTHING MENTALLY HOLDING ME BACK?
DID ANY LIMITING BELIEFS COME UP LAST WEEK?

WHY DO I THINK THIS IS?

WHAT EMPOWERING AFFIRMATION WILL HELP ME TO MOVE FORWARD OR REFRAME THIS LIMITING BELIEF?

FREE FLOW

WEEK BEGINNING ______________________

TO BE IN ALIGNMENT AND GROUNDED, THIS WEEK I WILL:

- ○ GO OUT IN NATURE
- ○ MEDITATE
- ○ ______________________
- ○ ______________________

I WILL RAISE MY VIBRATION WITH THE FOLLOWING ENERGIZING ACTIVITIES:

I AM GRATEFUL FOR:

____

I WOULD LIKE TO MANIFEST:

THE STEPS I CAN TAKE TO ACHIEVE THIS ARE:

- ○ ______________________
- ○ ______________________
- ○ ______________________

IS ANYTHING MENTALLY HOLDING ME BACK?
DID ANY LIMITING BELIEFS COME UP LAST WEEK?

WHY DO I THINK THIS IS?

WHAT EMPOWERING AFFIRMATION WILL HELP ME TO MOVE FORWARD OR REFRAME THIS LIMITING BELIEF?

FREE FLOW

* SACRED SPACE *

Record achievements no matter how big or small, reflect, or free-flow journal.

I LET GO OF ALL LIMITING BELIEFS

AND DO WHATEVER IT IS THAT
I FEEL ENERGETICALLY PULLED TO DO

WEEK BEGINNING ____________________

TO BE IN ALIGNMENT AND GROUNDED, THIS WEEK I WILL:

- ○ GO OUT IN NATURE
- ○ MEDITATE
- ○ ____________________
- ○ ____________________

I WILL RAISE MY VIBRATION WITH THE FOLLOWING ENERGIZING ACTIVITIES:

I AM GRATEFUL FOR:

____

I WOULD LIKE TO MANIFEST:

THE STEPS I CAN TAKE TO ACHIEVE THIS ARE:

- ○ ____________________
- ○ ____________________
- ○ ____________________

IS ANYTHING MENTALLY HOLDING ME BACK?
DID ANY LIMITING BELIEFS COME UP LAST WEEK?

WHY DO I THINK THIS IS?

WHAT EMPOWERING AFFIRMATION WILL HELP ME TO MOVE FORWARD OR REFRAME THIS LIMITING BELIEF?

FREE FLOW

WEEK BEGINNING ____________________

TO BE IN ALIGNMENT AND GROUNDED, THIS WEEK I WILL:

- ○ GO OUT IN NATURE
- ○ MEDITATE
- ○ ____________________
- ○ ____________________

I WILL RAISE MY VIBRATION WITH THE FOLLOWING ENERGIZING ACTIVITIES:

I AM GRATEFUL FOR:

____

I WOULD LIKE TO MANIFEST:

THE STEPS I CAN TAKE TO ACHIEVE THIS ARE:

- ○ ____________________
- ○ ____________________
- ○ ____________________

IS ANYTHING MENTALLY HOLDING ME BACK?
DID ANY LIMITING BELIEFS COME UP LAST WEEK?

WHY DO I THINK THIS IS?

WHAT EMPOWERING AFFIRMATION WILL HELP ME TO MOVE FORWARD OR REFRAME THIS LIMITING BELIEF?

FREE FLOW

WEEK BEGINNING ______________________

TO BE IN ALIGNMENT AND GROUNDED, THIS WEEK I WILL:

- ◯ GO OUT IN NATURE
- ◯ MEDITATE
- ◯ ______________________
- ◯ ______________________

I WILL RAISE MY VIBRATION WITH THE FOLLOWING ENERGIZING ACTIVITIES:

I AM GRATEFUL FOR:

____

I WOULD LIKE TO MANIFEST:

THE STEPS I CAN TAKE TO ACHIEVE THIS ARE:

- ◯ ____
- ◯ ____
- ◯ ____

IS ANYTHING MENTALLY HOLDING ME BACK?
DID ANY LIMITING BELIEFS COME UP LAST WEEK?

WHY DO I THINK THIS IS?

WHAT EMPOWERING AFFIRMATION WILL HELP ME TO MOVE FORWARD OR REFRAME THIS LIMITING BELIEF?

FREE FLOW

WEEK BEGINNING ______________________

TO BE IN ALIGNMENT AND GROUNDED, THIS WEEK I WILL:

◯ GO OUT IN NATURE ◯ MEDITATE

◯ ______________________ ◯ ______________________

I WILL RAISE MY VIBRATION WITH THE FOLLOWING ENERGIZING ACTIVITIES:

I AM GRATEFUL FOR:

____

I WOULD LIKE TO MANIFEST:

THE STEPS I CAN TAKE TO ACHIEVE THIS ARE:

◯ ____

◯ ____

◯ ____

IS ANYTHING MENTALLY HOLDING ME BACK?
DID ANY LIMITING BELIEFS COME UP LAST WEEK?

WHY DO I THINK THIS IS?

WHAT EMPOWERING AFFIRMATION WILL HELP ME TO MOVE FORWARD OR REFRAME THIS LIMITING BELIEF?

FREE FLOW

EEK BEGINNING ______________

TO BE IN ALIGNMENT AND GROUNDED, THIS WEEK I WILL:

- ○ GO OUT IN NATURE
- ○ MEDITATE
- ○ ______________
- ○ ______________

I WILL RAISE MY VIBRATION WITH THE FOLLOWING ENERGIZING ACTIVITIES:

I AM GRATEFUL FOR:

____

I WOULD LIKE TO MANIFEST:

THE STEPS I CAN TAKE TO ACHIEVE THIS ARE:

- ○ ______________
- ○ ______________
- ○ ______________

IS ANYTHING MENTALLY HOLDING ME BACK?
DID ANY LIMITING BELIEFS COME UP LAST WEEK?

WHY DO I THINK THIS IS?

WHAT EMPOWERING AFFIRMATION WILL HELP ME TO MOVE FORWARD OR REFRAME THIS LIMITING BELIEF?

FREE FLOW

✶ SACRED SPACE ✶

Record achievements no matter how big or small, reflect, or free-flow journal.

I AM ABUNDANT

WEEK BEGINNING ________________

TO BE IN ALIGNMENT AND GROUNDED, THIS WEEK I WILL:

- ◯ GO OUT IN NATURE
- ◯ MEDITATE
- ◯ ________________
- ◯ ________________

I WILL RAISE MY VIBRATION WITH THE FOLLOWING ENERGIZING ACTIVITIES:

I AM GRATEFUL FOR:

____

I WOULD LIKE TO MANIFEST:

THE STEPS I CAN TAKE TO ACHIEVE THIS ARE:

- ◯ ________________
- ◯ ________________
- ◯ ________________

IS ANYTHING MENTALLY HOLDING ME BACK?
DID ANY LIMITING BELIEFS COME UP LAST WEEK?

WHY DO I THINK THIS IS?

WHAT EMPOWERING AFFIRMATION WILL HELP ME TO MOVE FORWARD OR REFRAME THIS LIMITING BELIEF?

FREE FLOW

WEEK BEGINNING ____________________

TO BE IN ALIGNMENT AND GROUNDED, THIS WEEK I WILL:

- ◯ GO OUT IN NATURE
- ◯ MEDITATE
- ◯ ____________________
- ◯ ____________________

I WILL RAISE MY VIBRATION WITH THE FOLLOWING ENERGIZING ACTIVITIES:

I AM GRATEFUL FOR:

____

I WOULD LIKE TO MANIFEST:

THE STEPS I CAN TAKE TO ACHIEVE THIS ARE:

- ◯ ____________________
- ◯ ____________________
- ◯ ____________________

IS ANYTHING MENTALLY HOLDING ME BACK?
DID ANY LIMITING BELIEFS COME UP LAST WEEK?

WHY DO I THINK THIS IS?

WHAT EMPOWERING AFFIRMATION WILL HELP ME TO MOVE FORWARD OR REFRAME THIS LIMITING BELIEF?

FREE FLOW

* SACRED SPACE *

Record achievements no matter how big or small, reflect, or free-flow journal.

I FOLLOW THE PATH OF LEAST RESISTANCE

WEEK BEGINNING ____________________

TO BE IN ALIGNMENT AND GROUNDED, THIS WEEK I WILL:

- ○ GO OUT IN NATURE
- ○ MEDITATE
- ○ ____________________
- ○ ____________________

I WILL RAISE MY VIBRATION WITH THE FOLLOWING ENERGIZING ACTIVITIES:

I AM GRATEFUL FOR:

____

I WOULD LIKE TO MANIFEST:

THE STEPS I CAN TAKE TO ACHIEVE THIS ARE:

- ○ ____________________
- ○ ____________________
- ○ ____________________

IS ANYTHING MENTALLY HOLDING ME BACK?
DID ANY LIMITING BELIEFS COME UP LAST WEEK?

WHY DO I THINK THIS IS?

WHAT EMPOWERING AFFIRMATION WILL HELP ME TO MOVE FORWARD OR REFRAME THIS LIMITING BELIEF?

FREE FLOW

WEEK BEGINNING ______________________

TO BE IN ALIGNMENT AND GROUNDED, THIS WEEK I WILL:

- ◯ GO OUT IN NATURE
- ◯ MEDITATE
- ◯ ______________________
- ◯ ______________________

I WILL RAISE MY VIBRATION WITH THE FOLLOWING ENERGIZING ACTIVITIES:

I AM GRATEFUL FOR:

____

I WOULD LIKE TO MANIFEST:

THE STEPS I CAN TAKE TO ACHIEVE THIS ARE:

- ◯ ____
- ◯ ____
- ◯ ____

IS ANYTHING MENTALLY HOLDING ME BACK?
DID ANY LIMITING BELIEFS COME UP LAST WEEK?

WHY DO I THINK THIS IS?

WHAT EMPOWERING AFFIRMATION WILL HELP ME TO MOVE FORWARD OR REFRAME THIS LIMITING BELIEF?

FREE FLOW

* SACRED SPACE *

Record achievements no matter how big or small, reflect, or free-flow journal.

I AM BRAVE

WEEK BEGINNING ______________________

TO BE IN ALIGNMENT AND GROUNDED, THIS WEEK I WILL:

○ GO OUT IN NATURE ○ MEDITATE

○ ______________________ ○ ______________________

I WILL RAISE MY VIBRATION WITH THE FOLLOWING ENERGIZING ACTIVITIES:

I AM GRATEFUL FOR:

____

I WOULD LIKE TO MANIFEST:

THE STEPS I CAN TAKE TO ACHIEVE THIS ARE:

○ ____

○ ____

○ ____

IS ANYTHING MENTALLY HOLDING ME BACK?
DID ANY LIMITING BELIEFS COME UP LAST WEEK?

WHY DO I THINK THIS IS?

WHAT EMPOWERING AFFIRMATION WILL HELP ME TO MOVE FORWARD OR REFRAME THIS LIMITING BELIEF?

FREE FLOW

WEEK BEGINNING ____________________

TO BE IN ALIGNMENT AND GROUNDED, THIS WEEK I WILL:

- ◯ GO OUT IN NATURE
- ◯ MEDITATE
- ◯ ____________________
- ◯ ____________________

I WILL RAISE MY VIBRATION WITH THE FOLLOWING ENERGIZING ACTIVITIES:

I AM GRATEFUL FOR:

____

I WOULD LIKE TO MANIFEST:

THE STEPS I CAN TAKE TO ACHIEVE THIS ARE:

- ◯ ____
- ◯ ____
- ◯ ____

IS ANYTHING MENTALLY HOLDING ME BACK?
DID ANY LIMITING BELIEFS COME UP LAST WEEK?

WHY DO I THINK THIS IS?

WHAT EMPOWERING AFFIRMATION WILL HELP ME TO MOVE FORWARD OR REFRAME THIS LIMITING BELIEF?

FREE FLOW

✶ SACRED SPACE ✶

Record achievements no matter how big or small, reflect, or free-flow journal.

I HAVE EVERYTHING I NEED
TO MAKE MY DREAMS COME TRUE

WEEK BEGINNING ________________

TO BE IN ALIGNMENT AND GROUNDED, THIS WEEK I WILL:

- ◯ GO OUT IN NATURE
- ◯ MEDITATE
- ◯ ________________
- ◯ ________________

I WILL RAISE MY VIBRATION WITH THE FOLLOWING ENERGIZING ACTIVITIES:

I AM GRATEFUL FOR:

____

I WOULD LIKE TO MANIFEST:

THE STEPS I CAN TAKE TO ACHIEVE THIS ARE:

- ◯ ________________
- ◯ ________________
- ◯ ________________

IS ANYTHING MENTALLY HOLDING ME BACK?
DID ANY LIMITING BELIEFS COME UP LAST WEEK?

WHY DO I THINK THIS IS?

WHAT EMPOWERING AFFIRMATION WILL HELP ME TO MOVE FORWARD OR REFRAME THIS LIMITING BELIEF?

FREE FLOW

WEEK BEGINNING ______________________

TO BE IN ALIGNMENT AND GROUNDED, THIS WEEK I WILL:

◯ GO OUT IN NATURE ◯ MEDITATE

◯ ______________________ ◯ ______________________

I WILL RAISE MY VIBRATION WITH THE FOLLOWING ENERGIZING ACTIVITIES:

I AM GRATEFUL FOR:

____

I WOULD LIKE TO MANIFEST:

THE STEPS I CAN TAKE TO ACHIEVE THIS ARE:

◯ ____

◯ ____

◯ ____

IS ANYTHING MENTALLY HOLDING ME BACK?
DID ANY LIMITING BELIEFS COME UP LAST WEEK?

WHY DO I THINK THIS IS?

WHAT EMPOWERING AFFIRMATION WILL HELP ME TO MOVE FORWARD OR REFRAME THIS LIMITING BELIEF?

FREE FLOW

* SACRED SPACE *

Record achievements no matter how big or small, reflect, or free-flow journal.

I AM PROUD ♥ OF ♥ MYSELF

WEEK BEGINNING ____________________

TO BE IN ALIGNMENT AND GROUNDED, THIS WEEK I WILL:

- ○ GO OUT IN NATURE
- ○ MEDITATE
- ○ ____________________
- ○ ____________________

I WILL RAISE MY VIBRATION WITH THE FOLLOWING ENERGIZING ACTIVITIES:

I AM GRATEFUL FOR:

____

I WOULD LIKE TO MANIFEST:

THE STEPS I CAN TAKE TO ACHIEVE THIS ARE:

- ○ ____________________
- ○ ____________________
- ○ ____________________

IS ANYTHING MENTALLY HOLDING ME BACK?
DID ANY LIMITING BELIEFS COME UP LAST WEEK?

WHY DO I THINK THIS IS?

WHAT EMPOWERING AFFIRMATION WILL HELP ME TO MOVE FORWARD OR REFRAME THIS LIMITING BELIEF?

FREE FLOW

WEEK BEGINNING ____________________

TO BE IN ALIGNMENT AND GROUNDED, THIS WEEK I WILL:

- ○ GO OUT IN NATURE
- ○ MEDITATE
- ○ ____________________
- ○ ____________________

I WILL RAISE MY VIBRATION WITH THE FOLLOWING ENERGIZING ACTIVITIES:

I AM GRATEFUL FOR:

____

I WOULD LIKE TO MANIFEST:

THE STEPS I CAN TAKE TO ACHIEVE THIS ARE:

- ○ ____________________
- ○ ____________________
- ○ ____________________

IS ANYTHING MENTALLY HOLDING ME BACK?
DID ANY LIMITING BELIEFS COME UP LAST WEEK?

WHY DO I THINK THIS IS?

WHAT EMPOWERING AFFIRMATION WILL HELP ME TO MOVE FORWARD OR REFRAME THIS LIMITING BELIEF?

FREE FLOW

✷ SACRED SPACE ✷

Record achievements no matter how big or small, reflect, or free-flow journal.

I

RELEASE

* ALL *

THAT

NO

LONGER

SERVES ME

WEEK BEGINNING ______________

TO BE IN ALIGNMENT AND GROUNDED, THIS WEEK I WILL:

- ◯ GO OUT IN NATURE
- ◯ MEDITATE
- ◯ ______________
- ◯ ______________

I WILL RAISE MY VIBRATION WITH THE FOLLOWING ENERGIZING ACTIVITIES:

I AM GRATEFUL FOR:

____

I WOULD LIKE TO MANIFEST:

THE STEPS I CAN TAKE TO ACHIEVE THIS ARE:

- ◯ ______________
- ◯ ______________
- ◯ ______________

IS ANYTHING MENTALLY HOLDING ME BACK?
DID ANY LIMITING BELIEFS COME UP LAST WEEK?

WHY DO I THINK THIS IS?

WHAT EMPOWERING AFFIRMATION WILL HELP ME TO MOVE FORWARD OR REFRAME THIS LIMITING BELIEF?

FREE FLOW

WEEK BEGINNING ______________________

TO BE IN ALIGNMENT AND GROUNDED, THIS WEEK I WILL:

○ GO OUT IN NATURE ○ MEDITATE

○ ______________________ ○ ______________________

I WILL RAISE MY VIBRATION WITH THE FOLLOWING ENERGIZING ACTIVITIES:

I AM GRATEFUL FOR:

____

I WOULD LIKE TO MANIFEST:

THE STEPS I CAN TAKE TO ACHIEVE THIS ARE:

○ ____

○ ____

○ ____

IS ANYTHING MENTALLY HOLDING ME BACK?
DID ANY LIMITING BELIEFS COME UP LAST WEEK?

WHY DO I THINK THIS IS?

WHAT EMPOWERING AFFIRMATION WILL HELP ME TO MOVE FORWARD OR REFRAME THIS LIMITING BELIEF?

FREE FLOW

* SACRED SPACE *

Record achievements no matter how big or small, reflect, or free-flow journal.

I CAN
EASILY
TAP INTO
MY
MAGIC

WEEK BEGINNING ______________________

TO BE IN ALIGNMENT AND GROUNDED, THIS WEEK I WILL:

- ◯ GO OUT IN NATURE
- ◯ MEDITATE
- ◯ ______________________
- ◯ ______________________

I WILL RAISE MY VIBRATION WITH THE FOLLOWING ENERGIZING ACTIVITIES:

I AM GRATEFUL FOR:

____

I WOULD LIKE TO MANIFEST:

THE STEPS I CAN TAKE TO ACHIEVE THIS ARE:

- ◯ ______________________
- ◯ ______________________
- ◯ ______________________

IS ANYTHING MENTALLY HOLDING ME BACK?
DID ANY LIMITING BELIEFS COME UP LAST WEEK?

WHY DO I THINK THIS IS?

WHAT EMPOWERING AFFIRMATION WILL HELP ME TO MOVE FORWARD OR REFRAME THIS LIMITING BELIEF?

FREE FLOW

WEEK BEGINNING ______________

TO BE IN ALIGNMENT AND GROUNDED, THIS WEEK I WILL:

- ◯ GO OUT IN NATURE
- ◯ MEDITATE
- ◯ ______________
- ◯ ______________

I WILL RAISE MY VIBRATION WITH THE FOLLOWING ENERGIZING ACTIVITIES:

I AM GRATEFUL FOR:

____

I WOULD LIKE TO MANIFEST:

THE STEPS I CAN TAKE TO ACHIEVE THIS ARE:

- ◯ ______________
- ◯ ______________
- ◯ ______________

IS ANYTHING MENTALLY HOLDING ME BACK? DID ANY LIMITING BELIEFS COME UP LAST WEEK?

WHY DO I THINK THIS IS?

WHAT EMPOWERING AFFIRMATION WILL HELP ME TO MOVE FORWARD OR REFRAME THIS LIMITING BELIEF?

FREE FLOW

* SACRED SPACE *

Record achievements no matter how big or small, reflect, or free-flow journal.

flow

and never force

WEEK BEGINNING ______________________

TO BE IN ALIGNMENT AND GROUNDED, THIS WEEK I WILL:

- ○ GO OUT IN NATURE
- ○ MEDITATE
- ○ ______________________
- ○ ______________________

I WILL RAISE MY VIBRATION WITH THE FOLLOWING ENERGIZING ACTIVITIES:

I AM GRATEFUL FOR:

____

I WOULD LIKE TO MANIFEST:

THE STEPS I CAN TAKE TO ACHIEVE THIS ARE:

- ○ ____
- ○ ____
- ○ ____

IS ANYTHING MENTALLY HOLDING ME BACK?
DID ANY LIMITING BELIEFS COME UP LAST WEEK?

WHY DO I THINK THIS IS?

WHAT EMPOWERING AFFIRMATION WILL HELP ME TO MOVE FORWARD OR REFRAME THIS LIMITING BELIEF?

FREE FLOW

WEEK BEGINNING ____________________

TO BE IN ALIGNMENT AND GROUNDED, THIS WEEK I WILL:

- ◯ GO OUT IN NATURE
- ◯ MEDITATE
- ◯ ____________________
- ◯ ____________________

I WILL RAISE MY VIBRATION WITH THE FOLLOWING ENERGIZING ACTIVITIES:

I AM GRATEFUL FOR:

____

I WOULD LIKE TO MANIFEST:

THE STEPS I CAN TAKE TO ACHIEVE THIS ARE:

- ◯ ____________________
- ◯ ____________________
- ◯ ____________________

IS ANYTHING MENTALLY HOLDING ME BACK?
DID ANY LIMITING BELIEFS COME UP LAST WEEK?

WHY DO I THINK THIS IS?

WHAT EMPOWERING AFFIRMATION WILL HELP ME TO MOVE FORWARD OR REFRAME THIS LIMITING BELIEF?

FREE FLOW

* SACRED SPACE *

Record achievements no matter how big or small, reflect, or free-flow journal.

I take time
to notice the
ABUNDANCE
that I already
have
EVERY
DAY

WEEK BEGINNING ____________

TO BE IN ALIGNMENT AND GROUNDED, THIS WEEK I WILL:

- ○ GO OUT IN NATURE
- ○ MEDITATE
- ○ ____________
- ○ ____________

I WILL RAISE MY VIBRATION WITH THE FOLLOWING ENERGIZING ACTIVITIES:

I AM GRATEFUL FOR:

____

I WOULD LIKE TO MANIFEST:

THE STEPS I CAN TAKE TO ACHIEVE THIS ARE:

- ○ ____________
- ○ ____________
- ○ ____________

IS ANYTHING MENTALLY HOLDING ME BACK?
DID ANY LIMITING BELIEFS COME UP LAST WEEK?

WHY DO I THINK THIS IS?

WHAT EMPOWERING AFFIRMATION WILL HELP ME TO MOVE FORWARD OR REFRAME THIS LIMITING BELIEF?

FREE FLOW

WEEK BEGINNING ____________________

TO BE IN ALIGNMENT AND GROUNDED, THIS WEEK I WILL:

- ◯ GO OUT IN NATURE
- ◯ MEDITATE
- ◯ ____________________
- ◯ ____________________

I WILL RAISE MY VIBRATION WITH THE FOLLOWING ENERGIZING ACTIVITIES:

I AM GRATEFUL FOR:

____

I WOULD LIKE TO MANIFEST:

THE STEPS I CAN TAKE TO ACHIEVE THIS ARE:

- ◯ ____________________
- ◯ ____________________
- ◯ ____________________

IS ANYTHING MENTALLY HOLDING ME BACK?
DID ANY LIMITING BELIEFS COME UP LAST WEEK?

WHY DO I THINK THIS IS?

WHAT EMPOWERING AFFIRMATION WILL HELP ME TO MOVE FORWARD OR REFRAME THIS LIMITING BELIEF?

FREE FLOW

✴ SACRED SPACE ✴

Record achievements no matter how big or small, reflect, or free-flow journal.

I allow
my
INNER BEING
to guide
my
DECISIONS

WEEK BEGINNING ______________________

TO BE IN ALIGNMENT AND GROUNDED, THIS WEEK I WILL:

○ GO OUT IN NATURE ○ MEDITATE

○ ______________________ ○ ______________________

I WILL RAISE MY VIBRATION WITH THE FOLLOWING ENERGIZING ACTIVITIES:

I AM GRATEFUL FOR:

____

I WOULD LIKE TO MANIFEST:

THE STEPS I CAN TAKE TO ACHIEVE THIS ARE:

○ ____

○ ____

○ ____

IS ANYTHING MENTALLY HOLDING ME BACK?
DID ANY LIMITING BELIEFS COME UP LAST WEEK?

WHY DO I THINK THIS IS?

WHAT EMPOWERING AFFIRMATION WILL HELP ME TO MOVE FORWARD OR REFRAME THIS LIMITING BELIEF?

FREE FLOW

WEEK BEGINNING ____________________

TO BE IN ALIGNMENT AND GROUNDED, THIS WEEK I WILL:

- ◯ GO OUT IN NATURE
- ◯ MEDITATE
- ◯ ____________________
- ◯ ____________________

I WILL RAISE MY VIBRATION WITH THE FOLLOWING ENERGIZING ACTIVITIES:

I AM GRATEFUL FOR:

____

I WOULD LIKE TO MANIFEST:

THE STEPS I CAN TAKE TO ACHIEVE THIS ARE:

- ◯ ____________________
- ◯ ____________________
- ◯ ____________________

IS ANYTHING MENTALLY HOLDING ME BACK?
DID ANY LIMITING BELIEFS COME UP LAST WEEK?

WHY DO I THINK THIS IS?

WHAT EMPOWERING AFFIRMATION WILL HELP ME TO MOVE FORWARD OR REFRAME THIS LIMITING BELIEF?

FREE FLOW

✶ SACRED SPACE ✶

Record achievements no matter how big or small, reflect, or free-flow journal.

I RESPOND
TO MY
LIMITING BELIEFS
WITH
♥ KINDNESS ♥
AND PATIENCE

EEK BEGINNING ____________

TO BE IN ALIGNMENT AND GROUNDED, THIS WEEK I WILL:

- ◯ GO OUT IN NATURE
- ◯ MEDITATE
- ◯ ____________
- ◯ ____________

I WILL RAISE MY VIBRATION WITH THE FOLLOWING ENERGIZING ACTIVITIES:

I AM GRATEFUL FOR:

____

I WOULD LIKE TO MANIFEST:

THE STEPS I CAN TAKE TO ACHIEVE THIS ARE:

- ◯ ____________
- ◯ ____________
- ◯ ____________

IS ANYTHING MENTALLY HOLDING ME BACK?
DID ANY LIMITING BELIEFS COME UP LAST WEEK?

WHY DO I THINK THIS IS?

WHAT EMPOWERING AFFIRMATION WILL HELP ME TO MOVE FORWARD OR REFRAME THIS LIMITING BELIEF?

FREE FLOW

EEK BEGINNING ______________________

TO BE IN ALIGNMENT AND GROUNDED, THIS WEEK I WILL:

- ○ GO OUT IN NATURE
- ○ MEDITATE
- ○ ______________________
- ○ ______________________

I WILL RAISE MY VIBRATION WITH THE FOLLOWING ENERGIZING ACTIVITIES:

I AM GRATEFUL FOR:

____

I WOULD LIKE TO MANIFEST:

THE STEPS I CAN TAKE TO ACHIEVE THIS ARE:

- ○ ______________________________________
- ○ ______________________________________
- ○ ______________________________________

IS ANYTHING MENTALLY HOLDING ME BACK?
DID ANY LIMITING BELIEFS COME UP LAST WEEK?

WHY DO I THINK THIS IS?

WHAT EMPOWERING AFFIRMATION WILL HELP ME TO MOVE FORWARD OR REFRAME THIS LIMITING BELIEF?

FREE FLOW

SACRED SPACE

Record achievements no matter how big or small, reflect, or free-flow journal.

I KNOW I CAN

WEEK BEGINNING ____________________

TO BE IN ALIGNMENT AND GROUNDED, THIS WEEK I WILL:

○ GO OUT IN NATURE ○ MEDITATE

○ ____________________ ○ ____________________

I WILL RAISE MY VIBRATION WITH THE FOLLOWING ENERGIZING ACTIVITIES:

I AM GRATEFUL FOR:

____

I WOULD LIKE TO MANIFEST:

THE STEPS I CAN TAKE TO ACHIEVE THIS ARE:

○ ____________________

○ ____________________

○ ____________________

IS ANYTHING MENTALLY HOLDING ME BACK?
DID ANY LIMITING BELIEFS COME UP LAST WEEK?

WHY DO I THINK THIS IS?

WHAT EMPOWERING AFFIRMATION WILL HELP ME TO MOVE FORWARD OR REFRAME THIS LIMITING BELIEF?

FREE FLOW

WEEK BEGINNING ____________________

TO BE IN ALIGNMENT AND GROUNDED, THIS WEEK I WILL:

- ◯ GO OUT IN NATURE
- ◯ MEDITATE
- ◯ ____________________
- ◯ ____________________

I WILL RAISE MY VIBRATION WITH THE FOLLOWING ENERGIZING ACTIVITIES:

I AM GRATEFUL FOR:

____

I WOULD LIKE TO MANIFEST:

THE STEPS I CAN TAKE TO ACHIEVE THIS ARE:

- ◯ ____________________
- ◯ ____________________
- ◯ ____________________

IS ANYTHING MENTALLY HOLDING ME BACK?
DID ANY LIMITING BELIEFS COME UP LAST WEEK?

WHY DO I THINK THIS IS?

WHAT EMPOWERING AFFIRMATION WILL HELP ME TO MOVE FORWARD OR REFRAME THIS LIMITING BELIEF?

FREE FLOW

* SACRED SPACE *

Record achievements no matter how big or small, reflect, or free-flow journal.

I AM RESILIENT

WEEK BEGINNING ____________________

TO BE IN ALIGNMENT AND GROUNDED, THIS WEEK I WILL:

◯ GO OUT IN NATURE ◯ MEDITATE

◯ ____________________ ◯ ____________________

I WILL RAISE MY VIBRATION WITH THE FOLLOWING ENERGIZING ACTIVITIES:

I AM GRATEFUL FOR:

____

I WOULD LIKE TO MANIFEST:

THE STEPS I CAN TAKE TO ACHIEVE THIS ARE:

◯ ____________________

◯ ____________________

◯ ____________________

IS ANYTHING MENTALLY HOLDING ME BACK?
DID ANY LIMITING BELIEFS COME UP LAST WEEK?

WHY DO I THINK THIS IS?

WHAT EMPOWERING AFFIRMATION WILL HELP ME TO MOVE FORWARD OR REFRAME THIS LIMITING BELIEF?

FREE FLOW

WEEK BEGINNING ____________________

TO BE IN ALIGNMENT AND GROUNDED, THIS WEEK I WILL:

- ○ GO OUT IN NATURE
- ○ MEDITATE
- ○ ____________________
- ○ ____________________

I WILL RAISE MY VIBRATION WITH THE FOLLOWING ENERGIZING ACTIVITIES:

I AM GRATEFUL FOR:

____

I WOULD LIKE TO MANIFEST:

THE STEPS I CAN TAKE TO ACHIEVE THIS ARE:

- ○ ____________________
- ○ ____________________
- ○ ____________________

IS ANYTHING MENTALLY HOLDING ME BACK?
DID ANY LIMITING BELIEFS COME UP LAST WEEK?

WHY DO I THINK THIS IS?

WHAT EMPOWERING AFFIRMATION WILL HELP ME TO MOVE FORWARD OR REFRAME THIS LIMITING BELIEF?

FREE FLOW

* SACRED SPACE *

Record achievements no matter how big or small, reflect, or free-flow journal.

I confidently
flow with
my own
ideas & thoughts

WEEK BEGINNING ____________________

TO BE IN ALIGNMENT AND GROUNDED, THIS WEEK I WILL:

- ◯ GO OUT IN NATURE
- ◯ MEDITATE
- ◯ ____________________
- ◯ ____________________

I WILL RAISE MY VIBRATION WITH THE FOLLOWING ENERGIZING ACTIVITIES:

I AM GRATEFUL FOR:

____

I WOULD LIKE TO MANIFEST:

THE STEPS I CAN TAKE TO ACHIEVE THIS ARE:

- ◯ ____________________
- ◯ ____________________
- ◯ ____________________

IS ANYTHING MENTALLY HOLDING ME BACK? DID ANY LIMITING BELIEFS COME UP LAST WEEK?

WHY DO I THINK THIS IS?

WHAT EMPOWERING AFFIRMATION WILL HELP ME TO MOVE FORWARD OR REFRAME THIS LIMITING BELIEF?

FREE FLOW

WEEK BEGINNING ______________

TO BE IN ALIGNMENT AND GROUNDED, THIS WEEK I WILL:

- ○ GO OUT IN NATURE
- ○ MEDITATE
- ○ ______________
- ○ ______________

I WILL RAISE MY VIBRATION WITH THE FOLLOWING ENERGIZING ACTIVITIES:

I AM GRATEFUL FOR:

____

I WOULD LIKE TO MANIFEST:

THE STEPS I CAN TAKE TO ACHIEVE THIS ARE:

- ○ ______________
- ○ ______________
- ○ ______________

IS ANYTHING MENTALLY HOLDING ME BACK?
DID ANY LIMITING BELIEFS COME UP LAST WEEK?

WHY DO I THINK THIS IS?

WHAT EMPOWERING AFFIRMATION WILL HELP ME TO MOVE FORWARD OR REFRAME THIS LIMITING BELIEF?

FREE FLOW

✷ SACRED SPACE ✷

Record achievements no matter how big or small, reflect, or free-flow journal.

I believe in the power of following my intuition

WEEK BEGINNING ________________

TO BE IN ALIGNMENT AND GROUNDED, THIS WEEK I WILL:

- ○ GO OUT IN NATURE
- ○ MEDITATE
- ○ ________________
- ○ ________________

I WILL RAISE MY VIBRATION WITH THE FOLLOWING ENERGIZING ACTIVITIES:

I AM GRATEFUL FOR:

____

I WOULD LIKE TO MANIFEST:

THE STEPS I CAN TAKE TO ACHIEVE THIS ARE:

- ○ ________________
- ○ ________________
- ○ ________________

IS ANYTHING MENTALLY HOLDING ME BACK?
DID ANY LIMITING BELIEFS COME UP LAST WEEK?

WHY DO I THINK THIS IS?

WHAT EMPOWERING AFFIRMATION WILL HELP ME TO MOVE FORWARD OR REFRAME THIS LIMITING BELIEF?

FREE FLOW

WEEK BEGINNING ______________

TO BE IN ALIGNMENT AND GROUNDED, THIS WEEK I WILL:

○ GO OUT IN NATURE ○ MEDITATE

○ ______________ ○ ______________

I WILL RAISE MY VIBRATION WITH THE FOLLOWING ENERGIZING ACTIVITIES:

I AM GRATEFUL FOR:

____

I WOULD LIKE TO MANIFEST:

THE STEPS I CAN TAKE TO ACHIEVE THIS ARE:

○ ______________

○ ______________

○ ______________

IS ANYTHING MENTALLY HOLDING ME BACK?
DID ANY LIMITING BELIEFS COME UP LAST WEEK?

WHY DO I THINK THIS IS?

WHAT EMPOWERING AFFIRMATION WILL HELP ME TO MOVE FORWARD OR REFRAME THIS LIMITING BELIEF?

FREE FLOW

* SACRED SPACE *

Record achievements no matter how big or small, reflect, or free-flow journal.

I am
DEEPLY
IN TUNE
with my
WANTS
and
DESIRES

WEEK BEGINNING ______________________

TO BE IN ALIGNMENT AND GROUNDED, THIS WEEK I WILL:

- ○ GO OUT IN NATURE
- ○ MEDITATE
- ○ ______________________
- ○ ______________________

I WILL RAISE MY VIBRATION WITH THE FOLLOWING ENERGIZING ACTIVITIES:

I AM GRATEFUL FOR:

____

I WOULD LIKE TO MANIFEST:

THE STEPS I CAN TAKE TO ACHIEVE THIS ARE:

- ○ ____
- ○ ____
- ○ ____

IS ANYTHING MENTALLY HOLDING ME BACK?
DID ANY LIMITING BELIEFS COME UP LAST WEEK?

WHY DO I THINK THIS IS?

WHAT EMPOWERING AFFIRMATION WILL HELP ME TO MOVE FORWARD OR REFRAME THIS LIMITING BELIEF?

FREE FLOW

WEEK BEGINNING ____________________

TO BE IN ALIGNMENT AND GROUNDED, THIS WEEK I WILL:

- ◯ GO OUT IN NATURE
- ◯ MEDITATE
- ◯ ____________________
- ◯ ____________________

I WILL RAISE MY VIBRATION WITH THE FOLLOWING ENERGIZING ACTIVITIES:

I AM GRATEFUL FOR:

____

I WOULD LIKE TO MANIFEST:

THE STEPS I CAN TAKE TO ACHIEVE THIS ARE:

- ◯ ____________________
- ◯ ____________________
- ◯ ____________________

IS ANYTHING MENTALLY HOLDING ME BACK?
DID ANY LIMITING BELIEFS COME UP LAST WEEK?

WHY DO I THINK THIS IS?

WHAT EMPOWERING AFFIRMATION WILL HELP ME TO MOVE FORWARD OR REFRAME THIS LIMITING BELIEF?

FREE FLOW

✷ SACRED SPACE ✷

Record achievements no matter how big or small, reflect, or free-flow journal.

I CAN
EASILY
REFOCUS

WEEK BEGINNING ____________________

TO BE IN ALIGNMENT AND GROUNDED, THIS WEEK I WILL:

- ◯ GO OUT IN NATURE
- ◯ MEDITATE
- ◯ ____________________
- ◯ ____________________

I WILL RAISE MY VIBRATION WITH THE FOLLOWING ENERGIZING ACTIVITIES:

I AM GRATEFUL FOR:

____

I WOULD LIKE TO MANIFEST:

THE STEPS I CAN TAKE TO ACHIEVE THIS ARE:

- ◯ ____________________
- ◯ ____________________
- ◯ ____________________

IS ANYTHING MENTALLY HOLDING ME BACK?
DID ANY LIMITING BELIEFS COME UP LAST WEEK?

WHY DO I THINK THIS IS?

WHAT EMPOWERING AFFIRMATION WILL HELP ME TO MOVE FORWARD OR REFRAME THIS LIMITING BELIEF?

FREE FLOW

WEEK BEGINNING ____________________

TO BE IN ALIGNMENT AND GROUNDED, THIS WEEK I WILL:

- ○ GO OUT IN NATURE
- ○ MEDITATE
- ○ ____________________
- ○ ____________________

I WILL RAISE MY VIBRATION WITH THE FOLLOWING ENERGIZING ACTIVITIES:

I AM GRATEFUL FOR:

____

I WOULD LIKE TO MANIFEST:

THE STEPS I CAN TAKE TO ACHIEVE THIS ARE:

- ○ ____________________
- ○ ____________________
- ○ ____________________

IS ANYTHING MENTALLY HOLDING ME BACK?
DID ANY LIMITING BELIEFS COME UP LAST WEEK?

WHY DO I THINK THIS IS?

WHAT EMPOWERING AFFIRMATION WILL HELP ME TO MOVE FORWARD OR REFRAME THIS LIMITING BELIEF?

FREE FLOW

✷ SACRED SPACE ✷

Record achievements no matter how big or small, reflect, or free-flow journal.

I am
GRATEFUL
for everything
that I
already
have

WEEK BEGINNING ____________________

TO BE IN ALIGNMENT AND GROUNDED, THIS WEEK I WILL:

○ GO OUT IN NATURE ○ MEDITATE

○ ____________________ ○ ____________________

I WILL RAISE MY VIBRATION WITH THE FOLLOWING ENERGIZING ACTIVITIES:

I AM GRATEFUL FOR:

____

I WOULD LIKE TO MANIFEST:

THE STEPS I CAN TAKE TO ACHIEVE THIS ARE:

○ ____________________

○ ____________________

○ ____________________

IS ANYTHING MENTALLY HOLDING ME BACK?
DID ANY LIMITING BELIEFS COME UP LAST WEEK?

WHY DO I THINK THIS IS?

WHAT EMPOWERING AFFIRMATION WILL HELP ME TO MOVE FORWARD OR REFRAME THIS LIMITING BELIEF?

FREE FLOW

WEEK BEGINNING ______________

TO BE IN ALIGNMENT AND GROUNDED, THIS WEEK I WILL:

- ○ GO OUT IN NATURE
- ○ MEDITATE
- ○ ______________
- ○ ______________

I WILL RAISE MY VIBRATION WITH THE FOLLOWING ENERGIZING ACTIVITIES:

I AM GRATEFUL FOR:

____

I WOULD LIKE TO MANIFEST:

THE STEPS I CAN TAKE TO ACHIEVE THIS ARE:

- ○ ______________
- ○ ______________
- ○ ______________

IS ANYTHING MENTALLY HOLDING ME BACK?
DID ANY LIMITING BELIEFS COME UP LAST WEEK?

WHY DO I THINK THIS IS?

WHAT EMPOWERING AFFIRMATION WILL HELP ME TO MOVE FORWARD OR REFRAME THIS LIMITING BELIEF?

FREE FLOW

✶ SACRED SPACE ✶

Record achievements no matter how big or small, reflect, or free-flow journal.

*

I CAN

dream big

and I CAN

make it *

HAPPEN

*

WEEK BEGINNING ______________________

TO BE IN ALIGNMENT AND GROUNDED, THIS WEEK I WILL:

- ○ GO OUT IN NATURE
- ○ MEDITATE
- ○ ______________________
- ○ ______________________

I WILL RAISE MY VIBRATION WITH THE FOLLOWING ENERGIZING ACTIVITIES:

I AM GRATEFUL FOR:

____

I WOULD LIKE TO MANIFEST:

THE STEPS I CAN TAKE TO ACHIEVE THIS ARE:

- ○ ______________________
- ○ ______________________
- ○ ______________________

IS ANYTHING MENTALLY HOLDING ME BACK?
DID ANY LIMITING BELIEFS COME UP LAST WEEK?

WHY DO I THINK THIS IS?

WHAT EMPOWERING AFFIRMATION WILL HELP ME TO MOVE FORWARD OR REFRAME THIS LIMITING BELIEF?

FREE FLOW

WEEK BEGINNING ______________________

TO BE IN ALIGNMENT AND GROUNDED, THIS WEEK I WILL:

- ◯ GO OUT IN NATURE
- ◯ MEDITATE
- ◯ ______________________
- ◯ ______________________

I WILL RAISE MY VIBRATION WITH THE FOLLOWING ENERGIZING ACTIVITIES:

I AM GRATEFUL FOR:

____

I WOULD LIKE TO MANIFEST:

THE STEPS I CAN TAKE TO ACHIEVE THIS ARE:

- ◯ ______________________
- ◯ ______________________
- ◯ ______________________

IS ANYTHING MENTALLY HOLDING ME BACK?
DID ANY LIMITING BELIEFS COME UP LAST WEEK?

WHY DO I THINK THIS IS?

WHAT EMPOWERING AFFIRMATION WILL HELP ME TO MOVE FORWARD OR REFRAME THIS LIMITING BELIEF?

FREE FLOW

✴ SACRED SPACE ✴

Record achievements no matter how big or small, reflect, or free-flow journal.

I KNOW EXACTLY HOW TO GET TO WHERE I WANT TO BE

WEEK BEGINNING ______________________

TO BE IN ALIGNMENT AND GROUNDED, THIS WEEK I WILL:

- ◯ GO OUT IN NATURE
- ◯ MEDITATE
- ◯ ______________________
- ◯ ______________________

I WILL RAISE MY VIBRATION WITH THE FOLLOWING ENERGIZING ACTIVITIES:

I AM GRATEFUL FOR:

____

I WOULD LIKE TO MANIFEST:

THE STEPS I CAN TAKE TO ACHIEVE THIS ARE:

- ◯ ____
- ◯ ____
- ◯ ____

IS ANYTHING MENTALLY HOLDING ME BACK?
DID ANY LIMITING BELIEFS COME UP LAST WEEK?

WHY DO I THINK THIS IS?

WHAT EMPOWERING AFFIRMATION WILL HELP ME TO MOVE FORWARD OR REFRAME THIS LIMITING BELIEF?

FREE FLOW

WEEK BEGINNING ____________________

TO BE IN ALIGNMENT AND GROUNDED, THIS WEEK I WILL:

○ GO OUT IN NATURE ○ MEDITATE

○ ____________________ ○ ____________________

I WILL RAISE MY VIBRATION WITH THE FOLLOWING ENERGIZING ACTIVITIES:

I AM GRATEFUL FOR:

____

I WOULD LIKE TO MANIFEST:

THE STEPS I CAN TAKE TO ACHIEVE THIS ARE:

○ ____________________

○ ____________________

○ ____________________

IS ANYTHING MENTALLY HOLDING ME BACK?
DID ANY LIMITING BELIEFS COME UP LAST WEEK?

WHY DO I THINK THIS IS?

WHAT EMPOWERING AFFIRMATION WILL HELP ME TO MOVE FORWARD OR REFRAME THIS LIMITING BELIEF?

FREE FLOW

✷ SACRED SPACE ✷

Record achievements no matter how big or small, reflect, or free-flow journal.

I ACT

WEEK BEGINNING ______________

TO BE IN ALIGNMENT AND GROUNDED, THIS WEEK I WILL:

- ○ GO OUT IN NATURE
- ○ MEDITATE
- ○ ______________
- ○ ______________

I WILL RAISE MY VIBRATION WITH THE FOLLOWING ENERGIZING ACTIVITIES:

I AM GRATEFUL FOR:

____

I WOULD LIKE TO MANIFEST:

THE STEPS I CAN TAKE TO ACHIEVE THIS ARE:

- ○ ______________
- ○ ______________
- ○ ______________

IS ANYTHING MENTALLY HOLDING ME BACK?
DID ANY LIMITING BELIEFS COME UP LAST WEEK?

WHY DO I THINK THIS IS?

WHAT EMPOWERING AFFIRMATION WILL HELP ME TO MOVE FORWARD OR REFRAME THIS LIMITING BELIEF?

FREE FLOW

WEEK BEGINNING ______________________

TO BE IN ALIGNMENT AND GROUNDED, THIS WEEK I WILL:

- ◯ GO OUT IN NATURE
- ◯ MEDITATE
- ◯ ______________________
- ◯ ______________________

I WILL RAISE MY VIBRATION WITH THE FOLLOWING ENERGIZING ACTIVITIES:

I AM GRATEFUL FOR:

____

I WOULD LIKE TO MANIFEST:

THE STEPS I CAN TAKE TO ACHIEVE THIS ARE:

- ◯ ____
- ◯ ____
- ◯ ____

IS ANYTHING MENTALLY HOLDING ME BACK?
DID ANY LIMITING BELIEFS COME UP LAST WEEK?

WHY DO I THINK THIS IS?

WHAT EMPOWERING AFFIRMATION WILL HELP ME TO MOVE FORWARD OR REFRAME THIS LIMITING BELIEF?

FREE FLOW

WEEK BEGINNING ____________________

TO BE IN ALIGNMENT AND GROUNDED, THIS WEEK I WILL:

- ◯ GO OUT IN NATURE
- ◯ MEDITATE
- ◯ ____________________
- ◯ ____________________

I WILL RAISE MY VIBRATION WITH THE FOLLOWING ENERGIZING ACTIVITIES:

I AM GRATEFUL FOR:

____

I WOULD LIKE TO MANIFEST:

THE STEPS I CAN TAKE TO ACHIEVE THIS ARE:

- ◯ ____________________
- ◯ ____________________
- ◯ ____________________

IS ANYTHING MENTALLY HOLDING ME BACK?
DID ANY LIMITING BELIEFS COME UP LAST WEEK?

WHY DO I THINK THIS IS?

WHAT EMPOWERING AFFIRMATION WILL HELP ME TO MOVE FORWARD OR REFRAME THIS LIMITING BELIEF?

FREE FLOW

WEEK BEGINNING ______________________

TO BE IN ALIGNMENT AND GROUNDED, THIS WEEK I WILL:

◯ GO OUT IN NATURE ◯ MEDITATE

◯ ______________________ ◯ ______________________

I WILL RAISE MY VIBRATION WITH THE FOLLOWING ENERGIZING ACTIVITIES:

I AM GRATEFUL FOR:

____

I WOULD LIKE TO MANIFEST:

THE STEPS I CAN TAKE TO ACHIEVE THIS ARE:

◯ ____

◯ ____

◯ ____

IS ANYTHING MENTALLY HOLDING ME BACK?
DID ANY LIMITING BELIEFS COME UP LAST WEEK?

WHY DO I THINK THIS IS?

WHAT EMPOWERING AFFIRMATION WILL HELP ME TO MOVE FORWARD OR REFRAME THIS LIMITING BELIEF?

FREE FLOW

✷ SACRED SPACE ✷

Record achievements no matter how big or small, reflect, or free-flow journal.

I BELIEVE

✳ IN MY ✳

MAGIC

✱ ABOUT THE AUTHOR ✱

Photograph of the author by Joanne Crawford

Kelsey Layne is a designer and self-confessed journal/ stationery lover. As the founder of Note and Shine, she is bringing her vision of beautifully designed, user-friendly journals and paper products into the world, including *The Self-Love Journal* and *The Evening Rituals Journal*. She lives in York, England.